Spinosaurus
The roaring river

Written by Catherine Veitch

Illustrated by Leire Martin

Miles Kelly

Suki was the new dinosaur in the valley. She lived near a **roaring river** with her mum and dad.

With her huge sail, big snout and long claws, Suki looked fierce.

But all she wanted was to make some friends.

The other dinosaurs were afraid of Suki, and this made her **sad and lonely**.

One day Suki went for a walk through the valley. She spotted a little Bambiraptor who looked like she would make a **good** friend.

"Hello," she said. "I'm Suki, I'm **new** here."

But Suki's sail cast a huge shadow over the little Bambiraptor, whose name was Beth.

She was so frightened that she ran off without even saying her name.

Next, Suki came across a little Bagaceratops **chomping** on grass. A bird had landed on his bottom!

"Excuse me, **you have a bird on your bottom!**" laughed Suki.

The Bagaceratops, whose name was Billy, turned around and had the fright of his life...

HAHAHA!

...Suki's huge jaws were wide open as she roared with laughter. Billy plodded away as fast as he could.

On her way home Suki spotted an Avimimus. 'I'll try to make a friend one last time,' she thought.

Suki waved. But the Avimimus, whose name was Amy, took one look at Suki's **razor-sharp claws** and ran off.

At home, Suki felt sad.

"Why are you so sad?" asked her mum.

"No one wants to be my friend because they're scared of me," said Suki.

"Give them time to get to know you," said her mum. "Then, they'll see how lovely you are and they won't be scared anymore."

Suki felt **happier** after talking to her mum.
She ran off to find the other dinosaurs.

Beth, Billy and Amy were
playing by the **roaring**
river, so Suki went over
to say a proper hello.

WHOOSH!!!

The river suddenly burst its banks and water crashed over the young dinosaurs.

"HELP!" they yelled to Suki.

Suki staggered to her feet. She was just big enough to **stand up** in the water.

Beth was nearest to Suki. She **bravely** clung to a tree root.

Suki **struggled** against the water and waded over to Beth.

"Climb up my sail and hold on tight," Suki said gently. And she helped Beth onto her sail.

Further upstream, Billy clung to a log.

Suki pushed against the current to get to him.
It was **harder** now with Beth on her back.

"Keep still, don't be scared," Suki told Billy when she reached him.

Then she carefully picked him up in her huge jaws and held him above the water.

A long way upstream Amy was sprawled on a rock. The river was swirling around Suki. It was hard carrying both Beth and Billy.

But at last Suki reached Amy. Calmly she picked her up with her long claws.

Then with all three little dinosaurs safely in her care, Suki waded to the bank.

The dinosaurs' families were all waiting on the bank. They were so happy to see Suki and the **little dinosaurs** safely reach dry land.

"You're a real friend now," said Suki's mum with a smile. "But find a safer place to play away from the river."

The dinosaurs in the valley weren't afraid of Suki anymore. And Suki loved her brand new friends!